By the same author:

THE ART OF THINKING
DICTIONARY OF PHILOSOPHY
DICTIONARY OF THOUGHT
ON THE NATURE OF MAN
PICTORIAL HISTORY OF PHILOSOPHY
SPINOZA DICTIONARY
THE SOVIET IMPACT ON SOCIETY

A TREASURY OF WORLD SCIENCE